Where is it?

Is it here?

Yes. Here it is.

We can stop here.

Can we help?

Yes, you can.

Come in here, Ben.

Stop it, Digger.

Help. Stop, Digger.

Come here.

Where is Digger?

Is Digger in here?
No. Not in here.

Is Digger in here?

Yes. Look.

Digger is in here.

Here is my home.